Bangers and Mash.

1

Bangers is big.
Mash is little.

Bangers and Mash
sit on a rug.

Bangers has a red hat.

Mash has a blue hat.

Bangers gets a big box.

He puts his red hat
in the box.

Mash gets a pot of jam.

He puts his blue hat
in the jam.

Bangers puts his box
on his head.

10

Mash puts the jam pot
on his head.

Bangers can not get
the box off.

12

Mash has jam on his hat
and jam on his nose.

In comes Mum.
She gets the box off.

And she rubs the jam
off Mash's nose.

Bangers and Mash
run off with the box.